The Mouse Family
ABC

by Rosalind Sutton

Illustrated by Pamela Storey

W9-BYL-867

Brimax Books · Newmarket · England

Aa

A is for Apples;
All red and good to eat,
So Archie, Daisy, Don and Flo
Fill their baskets for a treat!

B b

B is for Ball;
The mice are having fun,
Don throws the ball and Daisy bats,
The others have to run.

Cc

C is for Clock;
The mice can tell the time,
They listen as the clock strikes one,
They like to hear it chime.

D d

D is for Duck;
She dabbles in a puddle,
Don tries to count the baby ducks,
But gets into a muddle.

Ee

E is for Engine,
It goes around the track,
The mice all like to have a ride,
They go forward, they go back.

Ff

F is for Frog;
It sits upon a leaf,
It sees the mice are watching it,
And jumps off with a leap.

G g

G is for Garden;
Flo makes her garden grow,
Moss at her feet, a toadstool seat
And flowers in a row.

Hh

H is for Hat;
The mice go to the park,
They put on boots and coats and hats,
Then play until it's dark.

Ii

I is for Ice-cream;
The mice like this a lot,
But they all laugh as Daisy says,
"Why can't we buy it hot?"

J j

J is for Jack-in-the-box;
Don wants to look inside,
The jack jumps out, Don gives a shout
And runs away to hide.

K k

K is for Kite;
The mice are holding tight,
For higher, higher up it goes,
It's almost out of sight.

L is for Letter;
"I'll read it out," says Don.
"An invitation out to lunch!"
They put their best clothes on.

M m

M is for Magician;
He makes a magic spell,
When it goes bang the mice hide from
The smoke and nasty smell.

N n

N is for Net;
Don takes his net and line
Down to the riverbank to fish,
He hopes the day stays fine.

Oo

O is for Otter;
Flo hides behind a tree,
The otter dives and swims about,
The others come to see.

P p

P is for Penguin;
The mice go to the zoo.
Don likes the way the penguins walk,
Flo watches what they do.

Q q

Q is for Queen;
She wears a golden crown,
She sits upon a royal throne,
The other mice bow down.

R r

R is for Rabbit;
He hops around the grass,
Don tries to run and catch him, but
He hops away too fast.

S s

S is for Sea;
It seems to touch the sky.
The mice sit on the sandy shore
To watch the ships go by.

T t

T is for Toys;
The mice are in their room,
They play with teddies, tops and trains
And bang a drum, boom, boom.

U u

U is for Umbrella;
The rain falls pitter patter,
But underneath the mice are dry,
So they just sit and chatter.

V v

V is for Violin;
Don plays a merry tune.
The other mice all like to dance
Beneath the silvery moon.

W w

W is for Wings;
The mice all try to fly.
They run and flap their tiny wings,
But cannot reach the sky.

X is for Xylophone;
An instrument to play,
The mice make merry music as
They tap and tap away.

Yy

Y is for Yacht;
Don sails out with his crew,
The other mice all hold on tight,
Don shows them what to do.

Z z

Z is for Zig-Zag;
The mice all love to ski,
They climb the slope, then zig-zag down
As happy as can be.